Why She Disappeared

When she fell, she fell apart.
Cracked her bones on the pavement she once decorated
as a child with sidewalk chalk
When she crashed, her clothes disintegrated and blew away
with the winds that took all of her fair-weather friends

When she looked around, her skin was spattered with ink
forming the words of a thousand voices,
Echoes she heard even in her sleep:
"Whatever you say, it is not right."
"Whatever you do, it is not enough."
"Your kindness is fake."
"Your pain is manipulative."

When she lay there on the ground,
She dreamed of time machines and revenge
and a love that was really something,
Not just the idea of something.

When she finally rose, she rose slowly
Avoiding old haunts and sidestepping shiny pennies
Wary of phone calls and promises,
Charmers, dandies and get-love-quick-schemes

When she stood, she stood with a desolate knowingness
Waded out into the dark, wild ocean up to her neck
Bathed in her brokenness
Said a prayer of gratitude for each chink in the armor
she never knew she needed
Standing broad-shouldered next to her
was a love that was really something,
not just the idea of something.

When she turned to go home,
She heard the echoes of new words
"May your heart remain breakable
But never by the same hand twice"
And even louder:
"without your past,
you could never have arrived—
so wondrously and brutally,
By design or some violent, exquisite happenstance
...here."

And in the death of her reputation,
She felt truly alive.

Poem by: Taylor Swift

SWIFT

Don't read the last page...

H ere's something I've learned about people.

We think we know someone, but the truth is that we only know the version of them they have chosen to show us. We know our friend in a certain light, but we don't know them the way their lover does. Just the way their lover will never know them the same way that you do as their friend. Their mother knows them differently than their roommate, who knows them differently than their colleague. Their secret admirer looks at them and sees an elaborate sunset of brilliant color and dimension and spirit and pricelessness. And yet, a stranger will pass that same person and see a faceless member of the crowd, nothing more. We may hear rumors about a person and believe those things to be true. We may one day meet that person and feel foolish for believing baseless gossip.

This is the first generation that will be able to look back on their entire life story documented in pictures on the internet, and together we will all discover the after-effects of that. Ultimately, we post photos online to curate what strangers think of us. But then we wake up, look in the mirror at our faces and see the cracks and scars and blemishes, and cringe. We hope someday we'll meet someone who will see that same morning face and instead see their future, their partner, their forever. Someone who will still choose us even when they see all the sides of the story, all the angles of the kaleidoscope that is you.

The point being, despite our need to simplify and generalize absolutely everyone and everything in this life, humans are intrinsically impossible to simplify. We are never just good or just bad. We are mosaics of our worst selves and our best selves, our deepest secrets and our favorite stories to tell at a dinner party, existing somewhere between our well-lit profile photo and our drivers license shot. We are all a mixture of selfishness and generosity, loyalty and self-preservation, pragmatism and impulsiveness. I've been in the public eye since I was 15 years old. On the beautiful, lovely side of that, I've been so lucky to make music for a living and look out into crowds of loving, vibrant people. On the other side of the coin, my mistakes have been used against me, my heartbreaks have been used as entertainment, and my songwriting has been trivialized as 'oversharing'.

When this album comes out, gossip blogs will scour the lyrics for the men they can attribute to each song, as if the inspiration for music is as simple and basic as a paternity test. There will be slideshows of photos backing up each incorrect theory, because it's 2017 and if you didn't see a picture of it, it couldn't have happened right?

Let me say it again, louder for those in the back...

We think we know someone, but the truth is that we only know the version of them they have chosen to show us.

There will be no further explanation.
There will just be **reputation**.

TA(y)BLE of CONTENTS

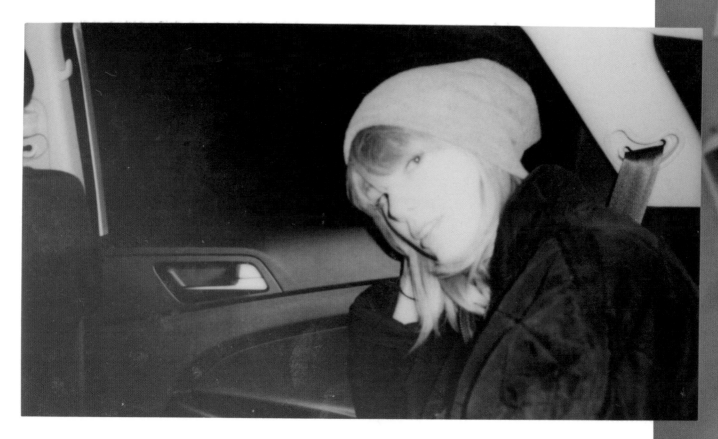

Executive Producer: Taylor Swift / Photography: Mert Alas, Marcus Piggot & Benny Horne / Wardrobe Stylist: Joseph Cassell / Hair: Paul Hanlon & Jemma Muradian Makeup: Isamaya Ffrench & Lorrie Turk / Manicurists: Lorraine Griffin & Kimmie Kyees / All Personal Photographs: Frosty Crew Photography Packaging Creative Direction: Taylor Swift / Packaging Art Direction: Josh & Bethany Newman / Packaging Design: Josh Newman, Austin Hale, Aaron Rayburn, Parker Foote, Ben Fieker for ST8MNT / Project Support & Coordination: 13 Management & Big Machine Teams

REP 5

REP 9

...READY FOR IT?

Knew he was a killer
First time that I saw him
Wondered how many girls
He had loved and left haunted

But if he's a ghost then,
I can be a phantom
Holding him for ransom

Some boys are tryin too hard
He don't try at all though
Younger than my exes

But he act like such a man so
I see nothing better
I keep him forever
... like a vendetta

I, I, I see how this is gon go
Touch me and you'll never be alone
I, island breeze and lights down low
No one has to know

In the middle of the night
In my dreams
You should see the things we do
Baby... Mmm...

In the middle of The night
In my dreams
I know I'm gonna be with you
So I take my time
... Are you ready for it?

Knew I was a robber
First time that he saw me
Stealing hearts and running off
And never saying 'sorry'
But if I'm a Thief Then
He can join the heist and
We'll move to an island
And. and he can be my 'jailer
Burton to This Taylor ♡
Every love I've known in comparison
is a failure
I forget their names now
I'm so very fame now
Never be The same now, now

Pre-chorus!
... Then another CHORUS

Bridge:
Baby let The games begin
Let The games begin
Let The games begin,
Baby let The games begin
Let The games begin
Let The games begin

... are you ready for it?

written by: Taylor Swift AKA Nils Sjöberg :)
Max Martin, song wizard
Shellback, mojo genius
Ali Payami; melodic ninja

END GAME

I wanna be your end game
I wanna be your first string
I wanna be your A Team
I wanna be your end game, end game

Big reputation, Big reputation
Ooh you and me, we got big reputations
Ah, and you heard about me
Ooh I got some big enemies
Big reputation, big reputation
Ooh you and me would be a big conversation
Ah, and I heard about you
Ooh, you like the bad ones too

(Future)

I don't wanna touch you
I don't wanna be
Just another ex love you don't wanna see
I don't wanna miss you
Like the other girls do
I don't wanna hurt you
I just wanna be
Drinkin on a beach with you all over me
I know what they all say
But I aint trying to play

(Ed Sheeran)

I hit you like BANG
We tried to forget it but we just couldn't
And I bury hatchets but I keep maps
of where I put 'em
Reputation precedes me
They told you I'm crazy
I swear I don't love the drama
It loves me

And I can't let you go
Your hand prints on my soul
It's like your eyes are liquor
It's like your body is gold.
You've been calling my bluff
On all my usual tricks
So here's the truth
from my red lips.

I wanna be your end game
I wanna be your first string
I wanna be your A Team
Wanna be your end game,
end game

Written by: Taylor Swift, Shellback,
Max Martin, Ed Sheeran, Future

ISLAND
BREEZE and
lights down low...

...no one has to
KNOW

REP 17

REP **19**

I DID
SOMETHING
BAD

I never trust a narcissist
But they love me.
So I play em like a violin
And I make it look oh so easy
'Cause for every lie I tell them,
they tell me three.
This is how the world works.
Now all he thinks about... is me.
I can feel the flames on my skin
Crimson red paint on my lips
If a man talks shit
Then I owe him nothing
I don't regret it one bit
'Cause he had it comin'.

They say I did something bad
Then why's it feel so good?
They say I did something bad
Then why's it feel so... good
Most fun I ever had.
And I'd do it over and over
and over again if I could
It just felt so... good... good...

I never trust a playboy
But they love me.
So I fly em all around the world
And I let them think they saved me.
They never see it coming
... What I do next
This is how the world works.
You gotta leave before you get left.
I can feel the flames on my skin.
He says "Don't throw away a good thing."
But if he drops my name
Then I owe him nothing
And if he spends my change,
Then he had it coming.

Chorus

They're burning all the witches
Even if you aren't one
They got their pitchforks and proof
Their receipts and reasons
They're burning all the witches
Even if you aren't one
So light me up, light me up
Light me up, go ahead and light me up.

Chorus

So bad, why's it feel so good?
Why's it feel - why's it feel so good...

Written by: Taylor, Max, Shellback

gorgeous ♡

♡

tiny baby James Reynolds, little cherubic
mischievous scene stealer from Heaven:
  " Gorgeous!

me, scraggly haired 27 yr old:

  You should take it as a compliment That I
Got drunk and made fun of The
  way you talk
  You should think about the
consequence of your magnetic field
bein a little too strong

  Annnd I got a boyfriend
  He's older than us
He's in The club doin I don't know what
You're so <u>cool</u> it makes me
  hate you so much

  whisky on ice, sunset and vine
  you've ruined my life
  By not being mine...
    * ding!*

  You're so gorgeous
I can't say anything to your face
Cause look at your face!
And I'm so furious
At you for making me feel this way
But what can I say?
  You're <u>gorgeous</u>.

You should take it as a compliment
That I'm talking to everyone here but you
You should think about the consequence of you
Touching my hand in a darkened room
If you got a girlfriend
I'm jealous of her
But if you're single...that's honestly worse
cause you're so gorgeous it actually hurts
Ocean blue eyes lookin in mine
I feel like I might
Sink and down and DIE.
               * Ding! *

          Chorus
You make me so happy
It turns back to sad
There's nothing I hate
More than what I cait have
You are so gorgeous
It makes me so mad
You make me so happy
It turns back to sad
There's nothing I hate
More then what I cait have
Guess I'll just stumble on home
  to my cats... alone ∵
...unless you want to come along?
               * Ding! *

          Chorus
Written by Shifty Swifty, Magic Max Martin,
          and Trixy Shellback

James

love

made

me

CRAZY

DON'T BLAME ME

I've been breaking hearts a long time
and toying with them older guys
Just playthings for me to use
Something happened for the first time
In the darkest little paradise
Shaking, pacing, I just need you.

For you, I would cross the line
I would waste my time
I would lose my mind
They say "She's gone too far this... time."

Don't blame me
Love made me crazy
If it doesn't, you ain't doin it right
Lord save me, my drug is my baby
I'll be using for the rest of my life
Don't blame me
Love made me crazy
If it doesn't, you ain't doin it right
Oh, Lord save me, my drug is my baby
I'll be using for the rest of my life

My name is whatever you decide and
I'm just gonna call you 'mine'.
I'm insane... but I'm your baby
Echoes of your name inside my mind
Halo! hiding my obsession
I once was poison ivy,
But now I'm your daisy.
And baby for you, I would fall from grace
Just to touch your face
If you walk away
I'd beg you on my knees to... stay.

Chorus ♡

I get so high (oh!)
Every time you're, every time you're
Loving me, you're loving me
Trip of my life (oh!)
Every time you're, everytime you're
touching me... you're touching me.
Every time you're, everytime you're loving me.
Oh Lord save me, my drug is my baby
I'll be using for the rest of my life.

♡

Written by: Taylor, Max and Johan
        (swift) (martin) (Shellback)

13

DELICATE

This ain't for the best.
My reputations never been worse so
you must like me for me.
We can't make any promises
Now can we babe
But you can make me a drink

Dive bar on the East Side
Where you at?
Phone lights up my nightstand
In the black
Come here, you can meet me
In the back
Dark jeans and your Nikes
Look at you
Oh Damn, never seen that color blue
Just think of the fun things we could do...
Cause I like you...
Yeah I want you...

Is it cool that I said all that?
Is it chill that you're in my head?
Cause I know that it's delicate
Is it cool that I said all that?
Is it too soon to do this yet?
Cause I know that it's delicate
Isn't it, isn't it, isn't it?

Third floor on the West Side
Me and you.
Handsome, you're a mansion with a view
Do the girls back home touch you
like I do?
Long night with your hands
Up in my hair
Echoes of your footsteps on the stairs
Stay here, honey
  I don't want to share
Cause I like you
Yeah I want you

  Chorus

Sometimes I wonder
when you sleep
Are you ever dreaming of me?
Sometimes when I look into your eyes
  I pretend you're mine
  all. The. damn. time.

Cause I like you.

  Written by Taylor, Max Martin, Shellback

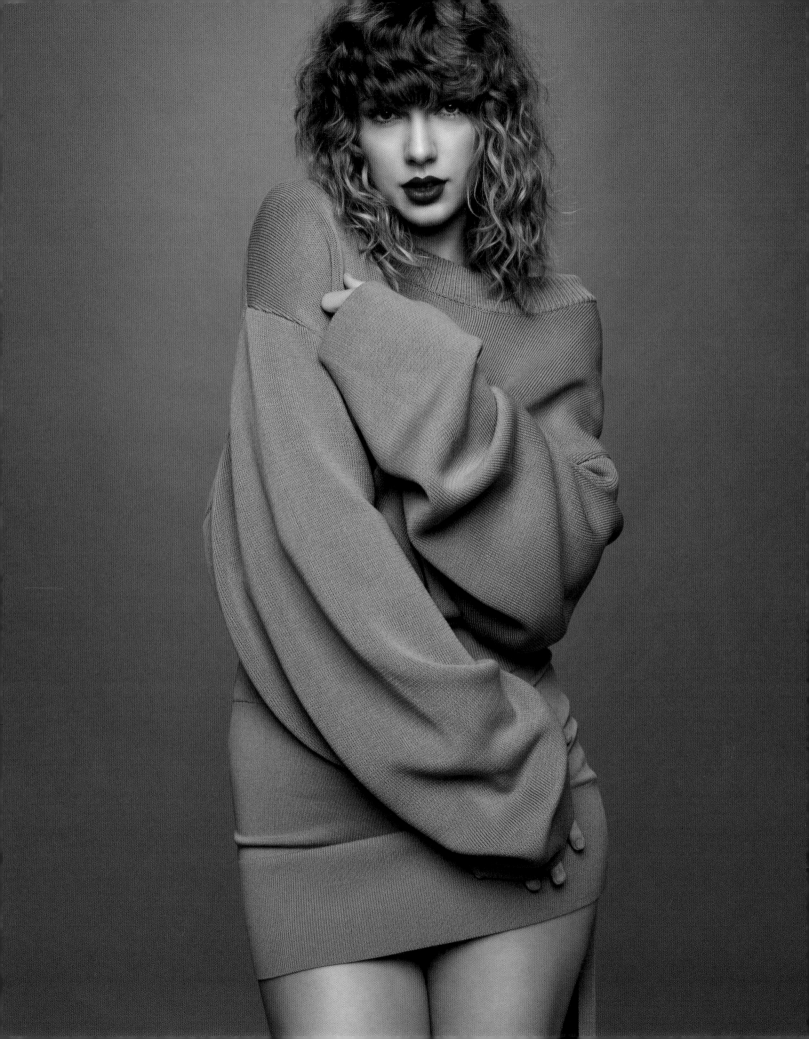

gold cage; hostage
to my feelings

SO IT *GOES...*

See you in the dark.
All eyes on you, my magician.
All eyes on us.
You make everyone disappear,
And cut me into pieces.
Gold cage, hostage to my feelings
Back against the wall
Trippin when you're gone
Cause we break down a little
But when you get me alone,
It's so simple.
Cause baby, I know what you know.
We can feel it...

And all the pieces fall
Right into place
Getting caught up in a moment
Lipstick on your face
♡ So it goes ♡
I'm yours to keep
And I'm yours to lose
You know, I'm not a bad girl
But I.. do bad things with you
♡ so it goes ♡

Met you in a bar.
All eyes on me, your illusionist
All eyes on us.
I make all your gray days clear
And wear you like a necklace.
I'm so chill but you make me jealous
But I got your heart
Skippin when I'm gone
Cause we break down a little
But when I get you alone
It's so simple
Cause baby I know what you know
We can feel it...

          Chorus

Come here, dressed in black now
So, so, so it goes
Scratches down your back now
So, so, so it goes

You did a number on me
But, honestly, baby
Who's counting?
I did a number on you
But, honestly, baby
Who's counting?

............1, 2, 3.

Written by Taylor Swift, Illusionist
        Max Martin, Sorcerer
        Shellback, Warlock
        Oscar Görres, Wizard

REP 43

LOOK WHAT YOU MADE ME DO

I don't like your little games
Don't like your tilted stage
The role you made me play
Of the fool
No, I don't like you

I don't like your perfect crime
How you laugh when you lie
You said the gun was mine
Isn't cool.
No I don't like you.

But I got smarter
I got harder in the nick of time
Honey, I rose up from the dead
I do it all the time
I got a list of names
And yours is in red, underlined
I check it once
Then I
check.
it.
twice.

Oh!

Oooh, look what you made me do
look what you made me do
look what you just made me do
look what you just made me-
Ooh, look what you made me do
Look what you made me do
Look what you just made me do
Look what you just made me-

I don't like your kingdom keys
They once belonged to me
You asked me for a place to sleep
Locked me out, and threw a feast
The world moves on
  Another day, another drama drama
But not far me
    Not far me
All I think about is karma
And then the world moves on
  But one things for sure
  Maybe I got mine
But you'll all. get. yours.

    Pre Chorus
    Chorus

I don't trust nobody
And nobody trusts me
I'll be the actress
Starring in your b<u>ad</u> <u>dreams</u>.

" I'm sorry. but the old Taylor
can't come to the phone right now...
why? Oh.
  Cause she's <u>dead</u>."

      Written by Taylor Swift, Jack Antonoff,
    Richard Fairbrass, Fred Fairbrass,
    Rob Manzoli

THIS IS WHY WE CAN'T HAVE NICE THINGS . . . BECAUSE YOU BREAK THEM

Legendary, Oscar-winning film special effects make-up artist Bill Corso (Deadpool, Star Wars Episode VII The Force Awakens) and his team spent 6 hours meticulously turning live Taylor into very, very dead Taylor.

Milky contacts were used to create the effect of frosted corpse eyes so Taylor was rendered almost completely blind for the zombie scenes.

Black ink was smeared on Taylor's teeth and gums to achieve the look of extreme decay and had to be continuously re-applied.

Taylor wore the actual dress from the "Out of the Woods" music video for this look. The make-up for Taylor's hands and feet included net sleeves and gloves, which elongated her fingers and toes, creating a skeletal appearance.

"I'M SORRY, *but the* OLD TAYLOR *can't come to the* phone RIGHT NOW..."

The faux diamonds used for this scene were actually a combination of a sequined blanket and thousands of plastic stones, as well as several pieces of antique jewelry strewn about on top.

Salute
to **Me**

I'm your

AMERICAN

Queen

A special effects team of dozens of CGI experts worked tirelessly for four months to create thousands of snakes for this scene.

REP 65

The dancers from The 1989 World Tour were asked to appear as extras in this scene as well as the vault scene and the birdcage scene.

HE CAN BE *my* JAILER,

BURTON to this TAYLOR

72 REP

The swing in this birdcage was 25 feet off the ground and required Taylor to be raised up by a lift and tethered to the swing for safety.

INTRODUCING

PHOTOGRAPHS

84 REP

The Trick to Holding On

Let go of the ones who hurt you
Let go of the ones you outgrow
Let go of the words they hurl your way
as you're walking out the door
The only thing cut and dry
In this hedge-maze life
Is the fact that their words will cut
but your tears will dry

They don't tell you this when you are young
You can't hold on to everything
Can't show up for everyone
You pick your poison
Or your cure
Phone numbers you know by heart
And the ones you don't answer any more

Hold on to the faint recognition in
the eye of a stranger
As it catches you in its lustrous net
How quickly we become intertwined
How wonderful it is to forget
All the times your intuition failed you
But it hasn't killed you yet
Hold on to childlike whims and moonlight
swims and your blazing self-respect

And if you drive the roads of this town
Ones you've gone down so many times before
Flashback to all the times
Life nearly ran you off the road
But tonight your hand is steady
Suddenly you'll know
The trick to holding on
Was all that letting go

Poem by: Taylor Swift

CONCLUDING

PHOTOGRAPHS

reputation

THIS IS WHY WE *CAN'T* HAVE *NICE THINGS*

It was so nice throwing big parties
Jump into the pool from the balcony
Everyone swimming in a champagne sea
And there are no rules when you show up here
Bass beat rattling the chandelier
Feeling so Gatsby for that whole year.
So why'd you have to rain on my parade?
I'm shaking my head
And locking the gates

This is why we can't have nice things
Darling
Because you break them
I had to take them away
This is why we can't have nice things
Honey
Did you think I wouldn't hear all the things
You said about me?
This is why we can't have... nice things

It was so nice being friends again
There I was giving you a second chance
But you stabbed me in the back
while shaking my hand
And therein lies the issue

Friends don't try to trick you

Get you on the phone
And mind-twist you
So I took an axe to a mended fence
But I'm not the only friend
You've lost lately
If only you weren't... so shady

Chorus

Here's a toast to my real friends
They don't care about the
he said / she said
And here's to my baby
He ain't reading what they call me lately
Here's to my mama
Had to listen to all this drama
And here's to you...
Cause forgiveness is a nice thing to do
* cackles * "I can't even say it
with a straight face!!"

Chorus
Oh, here's to my real friends
And here's to my baby
They didn't care about the he said/she said

Written by Taylor and Jack

REP **97**

GETAWAY CAR

It was the best of times
...the worst of crimes
I struck a match and blew your mind
But I didn't mean it,
And you didn't see it.
The ties were black, the lies were white
In shades of gray and candle light
I wanted to leave him.
I needed a reason.

X marks the spot where we fell apart
He poisoned the well
I was lying to myself.
I knew it from the first Old Fashioned
We were cursed.
We never had a shotgun shot in the dark.

You were driving the getaway car
We were flying, but we'd never get far
Don't pretend it's such a mystery.
Think about the place where you first met me.
Riding in a getaway car
There were sirens in the beat of your heart.
Should've known I'd be the first to leave
Think about the place where you first met me
In a getaway car
No, they never get far
No, nothing good starts in a getaway car.

It was the great escape, The prison break
The light of freedom on my face
But you weren't thinking
And I was just drinking.
Well, he was running after us.
I was screaming "Go, go, go!"
But with three of us, honey
It's a side show.
And a circus ain't a love story.
And now we're both sorry.
X marks the spot where we fell apart
He poisoned the well, every man for himself.
I knew it from the first Old Fashioned
We were cursed.
It hit you like a shotgun shot to the heart.

Chorus
We were jet set Bonnie and Clyde
Until I switched to the other side
It's no surprise, I turned you in.
Cause us traitors never win.

I'm in a getaway car
I left you in the motel bar
I put the money in a bag
And I stole the keys
That was the last time you ever saw me.

Chorus
I was riding in a getaway car, I was crying
In a getaway car, I was dying in a getaway car
said "goodbye" in a getaway car.

Written by Taylor Swift / Jack Antonoff

KING OF
MY HEART

I'm perfectly fine
I live on my own
I made up my mind
I'm better off bein alone
We met a few weeks ago
Now you try on calling me baby'
Like trying on clothes

Salute to me, I'm your American queen
And you move to me like I'm a Motown beat
And we rule the kingdom inside my room
Cause all the boys in their expensive cars
With their range ravers and their jaguars
Never took me quite where you do

And all at once
You are the one I have been waiting for
King of my heart, body, and soul
And all at once, you're all I want
I'll never let you go
King of my heart, body and soul
And all at once...
I've been waiting, waiting
And all at once you are the one
I've been waiting, waiting
Body and soul
And all at once

Late in the night
The city's asleep
Your love is a secret
I'm hoping, dreaming, dying to keep
Change my priorities
The taste of your lips is my idea
    of luxury

Pre Chorus

Chorus

    Is this the end of all the endings?
    My broken bones are mending
    With all these nights we're spending
    Up on the roof with a school girl crush
    Drinking beer out of plastic cups
    Say you fancy me, not fancy stuff
    Baby all at once, this is enough.

        Chorus

    Written by 2 Swedes and a Swift
        Max Martin, Shellback, Taylor Swift

DRESS

Our secret moments in a crowded room
They got no idea about me and you
There is an indentation in the shape of you
Made your mark on me, a golden tattoo
All of this silence and patience
Pining and anticipation
My hands are shaking from holding back from you
All of this silence and patience
Pining and desperately waiting
My hands are shaking from all this
Ah, Ah, Ah... Ahh...

Say my name and everything just stops.
I don't want you like a best friend
Only bought this dress
So you could take it off
Take it off.
Carve your name into my bedpost
Cause I don't want you like a best friend
Only bought this dress so you could
Take it off, take it off...

Inescapable
I'm not even gonna try
And if I get burned;
At least we were electrified
I'm spilling wine in the bath tub
You kiss my face
And we're both drunk
Everyone thinks that they know us

But they knew nothing about...
Pre chorus

Chorus

Flashback, when you met me
Your buzz cut and my hair bleached
Even in my worst times
You could see the best in me
Flashback to my mistakes
My rebounds, my earthquakes
Even in my worst lies,
You saw the truth in me.
And I woke up just in time
Now I wake up by your side
My one and only, my lifeline.
I woke up just in time
Now I wake up by your side
And my hands shake
I can't explain this....

Chorus
There is an indentation
In the shape of you
Made your mark on me... golden tattoo.

Written by: Taylor and Jack Antonoff

Nov 9
2016

How would you feel having
a song written about you? 4

DANCING WITH OUR HANDS TIED

I, I loved you in secret
First sight, yeah we love without reason
Oh, 25 years old
Oh, how were you to know
And my, my love had been frozen
Deep blue, but you painted me golden
Oh, and you held me close
Oh, how was I to know?

I could've spent forever with
Your hands in my pockets
Picture of your face
In an invisible locket
You said there was nothing in the world
That could stop it.
I had a bad feeling...
And darling you had turned my bed
Into a sacred oasis
People started talking
Putting us through our paces
I knew there was no one in the world
Who could take it
I had a bad feeling...

But we were dancing
Dancing with our hands tied, hands tied
Yeah we were dancing
Like it was The first time, first time
Yeah we were dancing
Dancing with our hands tied, hands tied

Yeah, we were dancing
And I had a bad feeling
...But we were dancing

I, I loved you in spite of
Deep fears that the world would divide us
So baby can we dance
Oh, Through an avalanche
And say, say that we got it
    I'm a mess, but I'm the mess That
       you wanted.
Oh, cause its gravity
Oh, Keeping you with me.
- - - - - - - - -
          Prechorus
- - - - - - - -
     Chorus
- - - - - - -

I'd kiss you as The lights went out
Swaying as The room burned down.
I'd hold you as the water rushes in
...If I could dance with you again
I'd kiss you as The lights went out
Swaying as The room burned down.
I'd hold you as The water rushes in
...If I could dance with you again.

          Chorus

Written by: Taylor Swift, Shellback,
          Max Martin, Oscar Holter

all my flowers grew
back as Thorns.

...yes.

You don't need to save me but would you run away with me?

CALL IT WHAT YOU *WANT*

My castle crumbled overnight
I brought a knife to a gun fight
They took the crown, but it's alright
All the liars are calling me one
Nobody's heard from me for months
I'm doing better than I ever was
Cause...

My baby's fit like a daydream
Walking with his head down
I'm the one he's walking to
So call it what you want, yeah
Call it what you want to
My baby's fly like a jet stream
High above the whole scene
Loves me like I'm brand new
So call it what you want, yeah
Call it what you want to

All my flowers grew back as thorns
Windows boarded up after the storm
He built a fire just to keep me warm
All the drama queens taking swings
All the jokers dressing up as kings
They fade to nothing when I look at him.
And I know I make the same mistakes
Every time, Bridges burn, I never learn
At least I did one thing right
I did one thing right.

I'm laughing with my lover
Making forts under covers
Trust him like a brother
Yeah, I know I did one thing right
Starry eyes sparking up my darkest night...

Chorus

I want to wear his initial
On a chain round my neck
Chain round my neck
Not because he owns me
But cause he really knows me
(which is more than they can say)
I recall late November
Holding my breath, slowly I said
"You don't need to save me,
but would you run away with me?"
...yes.

Written by Taylor Swift/Jack Antonoff

REP 127

128 REP

NEW YEAR'S DAY

There's glitter on the floor
After the party
Girls carrying their shoes
Down in the lobby
Candle wax and polaroids
On the hardwood floor
You and me from the night before

Don't read the last page
But I stay
When you're lost and I'm scared
And you're turning away
I want your midnights
But I'll be cleaning up bottles with you
On New Years Day

You squeeze my hand three times
In the back of the taxi
I can tell that it's gonna be
a long road.
I'll be there if you're the
toast of the town, babe
Or if you strike out
and you're crawling home.

Don't read the last page
But I stay when it's hard
Or it's wrong and we're making mistakes
I want your midnights
But I'll be cleaning up bottles with you
On New Years Day

Hold on to The memories,
They will hold onto you... ×3
And I will hold onto you.

Please don't ever become a stranger
Whose laugh I could recognize anywhere.

There's glitter on The floor
After the party
Girls carrying Their shoes
Down in The lobby
Candlewax and polaroids
On The hardwood floor

... you and me, forevermore.

Written by Taylor and Jack, as his
dogs Karen and Susan looked on.

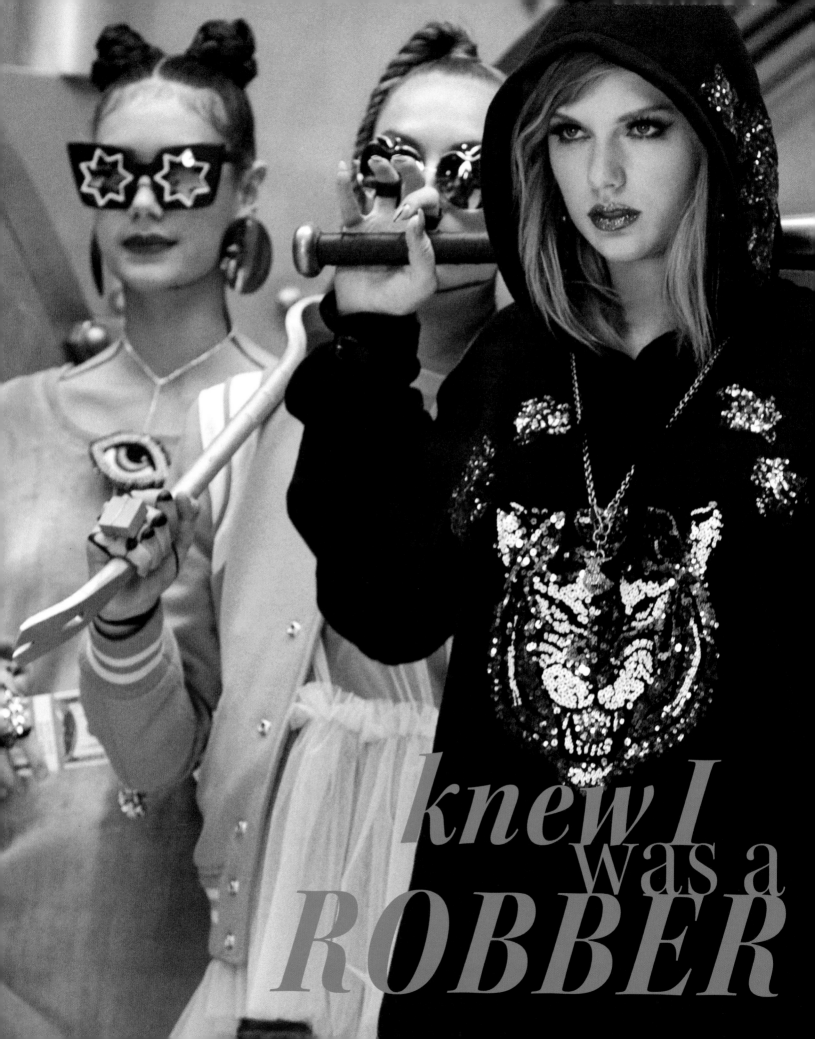

knew I was a ROBBER

FIRST TIME THAT HE SAW ME

I NEVER TRUST
a narcissist

BUT THEY

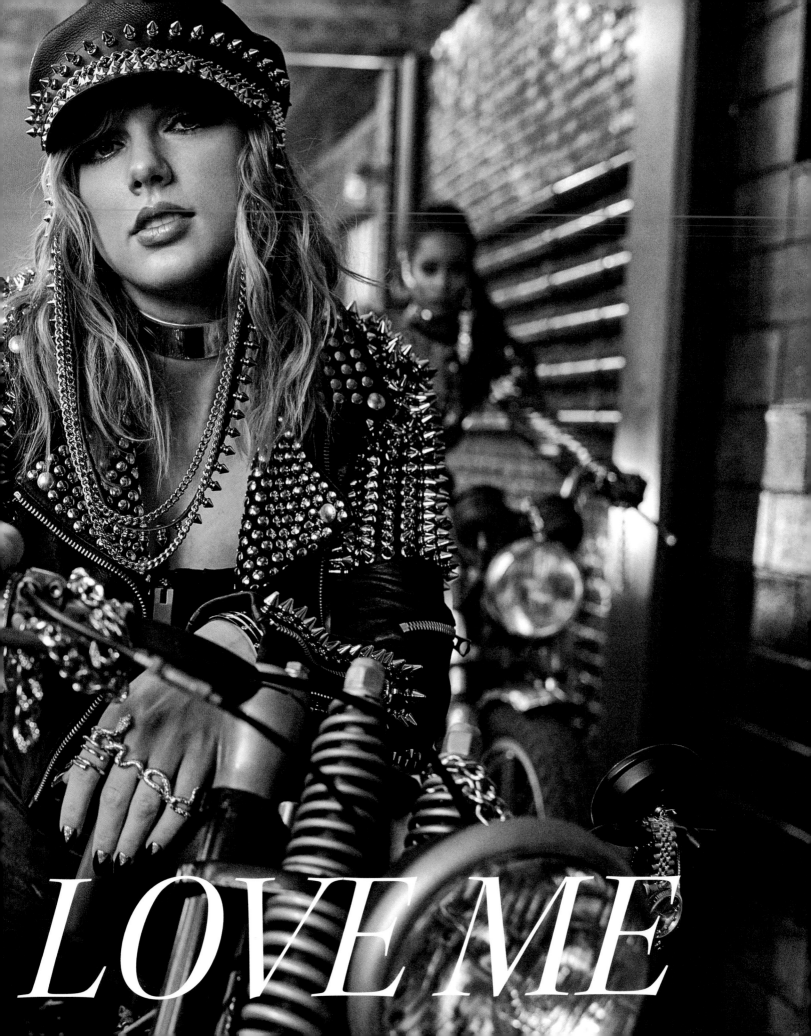

LOVE ME

Taylor's music video director and long-term collaborator Joseph Kahn returns for their most ambitious project to date.

BUT I GOT *smarter,* I GOT *HARDER*

IN THE *NICK* *of* TIME

YOU'RE

146 REP

SO GORGEOUS

I CAN'T *say* ANYTHING TO YOUR *face*

REP 149

Taylor secretly snuck into rehearsal facilities in both London and LA in order to prepare for the video shoot.

most fun
I EVER
HAD.

I'LL BE
the actress

STARRING
IN YOUR *BAD
DREAMS*

Actresses were hired to be Taylor look-a-likes in order to represent "the old Taylor." As soon as the cameras stopped rolling on some of these fight scenes, the entire cast and crew laughed hysterically.

If You're Anything Like Me

If you're anything like me,
You bite your nails,
And laugh when you're nervous.
You promise people the world,
because that's what they want from you.
You like giving them what they want...
But darling, you need to stop.

If you're anything like me,
You knock on wood every time you make plans.
You cross your fingers, hold your breath,
Wish on lucky numbers and eyelashes
Your superstitions were the lone survivors of the shipwreck.
Rest In Peace, to your naive bravado...
If life gets too good now,
Darling, it scares you.

If you're anything like me,
You never wanted to lock your door,
Your secret garden gate or your diary drawer
Didn't want to face the you you don't know anymore
For fear she was much better before...
But Darling, now you have to.

If you're anything like me,
There's a justice system in your head
For names you'll never speak again,
And you make your ruthless rulings.
Each new enemy turns to steel
They become the bars that confine you,
In your own little golden prison cell...
But Darling, there is where you meet yourself.

If you're anything like me
You've grown to hate your pride
To love your thighs
And no amount of friends at 25
Will fill the empty seats
At the lunch tables of your past
The teams that picked you last...
But Darling, you keep trying.

If you're anything like me,
You couldn't recognize the face of love
Until they stripped you of your shiny paint
Threw your victory flag away
And you saw the ones who wanted you anyway...
Darling, later on you will thank your stars
for that frightful day.

If you're anything like me,
I'm sorry.

But Darling, it's going to be okay.

Poem by: Taylor Swift

... but

SWIFT

stay.